# CONSUMER MATHEMATICS 6
# SERVICE OCCUPATIONS

## CONTENTS

| | |
|---|---|
| **Author:** | **Thomas W. Hazard, Ph.D.** |
| Editor-in-Chief: | Richard W. Wheeler, M.A.Ed. |
| Editor: | Stephany L. Sykes |
| Consulting Editor: | Robert L. Zenor, M.A., M.S. |
| Illustrator: | Thomas R. Rush |

AOP

804 N. 2nd Ave. E., Rock Rapids, IA 51246-1759
© MCMLXXIX by Alpha Omega Publications, Inc. All rights reserved.
LIFEPAC is a registered trademark of Alpha Omega Publications, Inc.

# SERVICE OCCUPATIONS

The service occupations comprise an increasingly important classification in terms of this nation's labor force. With the latest available data, the Bureau of Labor Statistics indicates that over 14 million people are employed in service-related jobs. The projected growth calls for a 55 per cent increase in this sector during the next ten years, the highest for any sector.

What are the service-related jobs? Specifically, the term *services* includes jobs engaged in necessary support activities. Examples are food services, protective services, automotive services, accounting services, insurance services, hotel services, and travel services, to name just a few.

Like any other occupation, these jobs require an understanding of basic mathematical principles and the ability to apply these principles in day-to-day activities. Therefore, as you proceed through this LIFEPAC, you will be exposed not only to fundamental mathematical operations but also to practical work-related applications. In an effort to fix firmly the principles in your mind, we shall provide you with meaningful practice in applying mathematical concepts and procedures.

## OBJECTIVES

**Read these objectives.** The objectives tell you what you will be able to do when you have successfully completed this LIFEPAC.

When you have finished this LIFEPAC, you should be able

1. To figure change due in money transactions,

2. To figure the amount of sales tax,

3. To compute interest charges,

4. To figure discounts and markups,

5. To interpret data in tabular form,

6. To perform line-graph analysis,

7. To perform bar-graph analysis,

8. To estimate service facility capacity,

9. To apply correct mathematical operations in specific occupations, and

10. To determine prices for services rendered.

**Survey the LIFEPAC.** Ask yourself some questions about this study. Write your questions here.

_____

_____

_____

_____

_____

_____

_____

_____

_____

---

## I. FINANCIAL TRANSACTIONS

### OBJECTIVES

1. To figure change due in money transactions.
2. To figure the amount of sales tax.
3. To compute interest charges.
4. To figure discounts and markups.

---

Financial transactions are an essential part of service occupations. A great deal of service employees' exposure to the consumer is directly related to money and credit transactions. The ability to figure cash transactions, such as how to make change and total receipts, is fundamental to effective job performance.

Credit transactions are a little more complicated than cash transactions, in that one must work with percentages and fractions to compute interest charges and time payments.

This section tells how to make change, an important and common cash transaction.

---

PROCEDURE

To make change, subtract the total charges from the amount *tendered* in payment, and give back the difference in bills or coins or both.

---

Model 1:   A woman gives her hairdresser a twenty-dollar bill when quoted a price of $7.50. How will the hairdresser make change?

Since the transaction is for $7.50 and a $20 bill has been tendered, the hairdresser will subtract $7.50 from $20.00 and return the difference to the customer.

Amount tendered = $20.00
Less your cost = − 7.50
Change returned = $12.50

Model 2:   You render a service for $8.75. You are given $10.00 in payment. How much should you return in change?

Amount tendered = $10.00
Less your cost = − 8.75
Change returned = $ 1.25

■■■■   Perform the following change calculations.

1.1   Charge is $12.82. The customer gave $15.00.

Compute the change.   _____

1.2   Charge is $6.98. The customer gave $10.00.

How much change?   _____

1.3   Charge is $3.84. The customer tendered $5.00.

Figure the correct change._____

1.4   Price is $4.00. Find the amount of change due from a

$5 bill tendered.   _____

3

Truth-in-lending legislation requires the lender or extender of credit to quote not only the interest rate, but also the annual percentage rate and the finance charges in dollars. The interest rate, expressed in terms of a monthly rate, will frequently be lower than the annual percentage rate. We shall be concerned only with the annual percentage rate, which is the true annual interest rate.

---

PROCEDURE

To calculate the true annual interest rate, multiply two times the number of payments made in a year ($y$) by the total amount of interest charges ($c$); divide the result by the product of the amount financed ($m$) and the number of payments to be made over the life of the contract ($n$) plus one.

$$I = \frac{2(yc)}{m(n + 1)}$$

---

Model 1: Compute the true annual interest rate on an installment contract where the payments of $28.50 are made monthly for a period of 36 months, and the amount financed is $935.

Total payments made for 36 months = 36 x $28.50 = $1,026.

Total amount of interest = $1,026 - 935 = $91.

$$I = \frac{2(12 \text{ x } 91)}{935(36 + 1)} = \frac{2,184}{34,595}$$

Therefore, $I$ = 0.063, or 6.3%.

Model 2: Compute the *principal* plus interest payments necessary to retire a note for $1,000, if 24 equal monthly payments are made and a 7.5% true annual interest rate is charged.

$$I = \frac{2(yc)}{m(n + 1)}; \quad 0.075 = \frac{2(12 \text{ x } c)}{1,000(24 + 1)}$$

$$c = \frac{1,875}{24}$$

Therefore, $c$ = $78.13

Since the total interest charges amount to $78.13,

$$\text{monthly payments} = \frac{1,000 + 78.13}{24}$$

$$= \$44.92.$$

6

Work the following true annual interest problems.

1.13  $c = \$158.15$; $y = 12$; $m = \$2{,}500$; $n = 36$.  Find $I$.

---

1.14  $c = \$88.18$; $y = 12$; $m = \$1{,}100$; $n = 18$.  Find $I$.

---

1.15  $I = 18\%$; $y = 12$; $m = \$600$; $n = 24$.  Find $c$.

---

1.16  $I = 12\%$; $y = 12$; $m = \$275$; $n = 18$.  Find interest charges.

---

1.17  A customer buys an automobile from you, the salesman. The price of the car, which includes taxes and license, amounts to $5,955.00. The customer wants to finance the car over 48 months after making a $500 down payment. You inform him that the true annual interest rate is 18%. He wants to know what his payments will be. What are the monthly payments (principal plus interest)?

---

1.18  Compute the true annual interest rate charged for a loan of $3,500, paid off in 36 equal payments of $104.50.

---

## ∿∿∿∿∿ DISCOUNTS AND MARKUPS ∿∿∿∿∿∿∿∿∿∿

*Discounts* and *markups* are widespread throughout businesses and occupations. Merchants habitually adjust list prices of their merchandise to increase sales, to provide incentives for cash payment, and to sell slow-moving goods. Merchants make these adjustments through a technique known as discounting. Discounting is deducting a certain percentage of the amount of cost. Cash discounts are also given for early payment on credit accounts.

To establish the selling price of a commodity, the merchant employs the technique of markup. Markup is the percentage or amount added to the cost of his goods to take care of *profit* and *overhead*.

Even though both techniques employ a percentage increase or decrease, their correct applications can pose problems for the beginner. We will take each technique in turn.

PROCEDURE

To determine the amount of discount, multiply the list price by the percentage rate of the discount. To obtain the discount price, deduct the discount amount from the list price.

Model 1: A 10% discount is offered on a certain item that sells for $10.95. How much is the discount and what is the discounted sales price?

a. Amount of discount = (0.10)($10.95) = $1.10.

b. Discounted sales price = $10.95 - 1.10 = $9.85.

(Note: If you were interested only in the discounted sales price, you could find the answer directly by multiplying the retail price ($10.95) by (1 - 0.10): $10.95(0.90) = $9.85.)

Model 2: A store offers you a 2% discount if you pay your bill of $185 within ten days of billing. How much will you have to pay to take advantage of this discount?

Amount to pay = $185.00 - (0.02)(185)
= $185.00 - 3.70
= $181.30.

Model 3:   The retail price on an article is $65.75.
If you offer to sell it for $62.50, what
percentage discount are you offering?

(% discount)($65.75) = $65.75 - 62.50

% discount = $\frac{3.25}{65.75}$ = 0.0494 or 5%

---

PROCEDURE

To set a price when cost and desired markup as a percentage
of a retail price are known, multiply the cost by the percent
markup to give the markup dollar amount.  Then add the dollar
markup to the cost to give the selling price.

Price = (cost x % markup) + cost

cost x % markup = dollar amount of markup

selling price = markup dollar amount + cost

---

Model 1:   A merchant wants to establish the selling
price of an item that costs him $4.50 so
that he will achieve a 15% markup.  What
is his selling price?

Price = ($4.50 x .15) + $4.50

Price = $0.68 + $4.50 = $5.18

Model 2:   A good you wish to purchase is sale priced at
$9.95.  You find out that the list price for
the same good is $9.15.  What is the markup
percentage used?

$9.95 = ($9.15 x % markup) + $9.15

$9.95 - $9.15 = $9.15 x % markup

$0.80 = $9.15 x % markup

$\frac{\$0.80}{\$9.15}$ = .087 = 9%

■■■   Compute the following discounts and markups.

1.19   Retail price = $15.75
Discount = 12.5%
How much is the discount? _____

1.20   Retail price = $4,595
Discount = 15%
How much is the discount? _____

9

1.21    Retail price = $475
        Amount of discount = $45
        What percentage discount is offered?

        _____

1.22    Amount of discount = $35
        Percentage of discount = 10%
        What is the  original list price?
        (Hint:  Divide amount of discount by
        discount rate.)

        _____

1.23    An article sells for $415.80.  You wish to discount

        it at 20%.  At what price will you offer it after

        discount?                _____

1.24    You are offered an item for $17.85.  The seller states

        he normally sells the same item for $19.95.  What

        percentage discount is he offering you?

        _____

1.25    Cost = $38.75
        Desired markup = 10%
        What is the price after markup?

        _____

1.26    Cost = $138.25
        Desired markup = 12.5%
        What is the price after markup?

        _____

1.27    Cost = $58.00
        Price after markup = $63.00
        What is the desired markup (percentage)?

        _____

1.28    Price after markup = $75.50
        Markup used = 5%
        What is the cost?

        _____

1.29　You see a used car you wish to buy. The dealer quotes

you a price of $1,595. You have a blue book quotation

of $1,435 for the same model and year. How much markup

is the dealer using?　_____

1.30　The flat rate of your service runs $6.50 per hour. To

cover overhead, you charge a markup of 15% for the first

8 hours, and 10% on the second 8 hours. You estimate

that a particular job will take you 16 hours. What

price will you submit to your client? (Hint: Find

the price with a 15% markup, and the price with a 10%

markup. Add the two results together to get the

total price.)　_____

---

Review the material in this section in preparation for the Self Test. The Self
Test will check your mastery of this particular section. The items missed on this
Self Test will indicate specific areas where restudy is needed for mastery.

## SELF TEST 1

Figure the change due in the following cash transactions (each
answer, 3 points).

1.01　The bill is $19.43. Payment tendered is $20. How

much change?　_____

1.02　You charge a customer $62.48 for an article. He gives

you a check for $100. How much change is due him?

_____

1.03    An item costs $42.28.  All you have in cash are three

$20 bills.  How much change should you receive in the

transaction?    _____

Compute the sales tax on the following transactions (each answer,
3 points).

1.04    An article retails for $38.50.  The city sales tax is

4%, and the federal excise tax is 7%.  How much is the

total tax?    _____

1.05    A seat to a musical costs $5.50.  To that amount

must be added a 6% entertainment tax.  How much money

must you receive in total to give a customer a ticket?

_____

1.06    The total price of an article is $7.02, including tax.

If the tax rate is 8%, what is the retail price of the

article?    _____

1.07    A certain car costs $6,595 before taxes are added.  Taxes

are $460 and license tags cost $55.  What is the tax

rate?    _____

Compute the following true annual interest rate problems (each
answer, 4 points).

1.08    Loan amount = $10,000
         Monthly payments = $258.50
         Time of loan contract = 5 years
         True annual interest rate?

_____

1.09    Purchase price of article = $495
         Down payment = $50
         Number of payments = 36
         True annual interest rate = 18%
         Monthly payment amount?

_____

1.010   You purchase a cafeteria business for $15,000. You put $2,250 down and finance the rest to pay off the loan in 5 years at 12% true annual interest. What are your monthly payments to pay off the loan?

_____

Compute the discounts and markups for the following problems (each answer, 4 points).

1.011   Cost of article = $195
        Retail price = $225
        Percentage of markup?

_____

1.012   List price of article = $2,150
        Percentage discount = 18%
        Retail price?

_____

1.013   Cost of article = $455
        Percentage of markup = 28%
        Retail price?

_____

1.014   Retail price of article = $555
        Percentage of markup = 35%
        Cost of article?

_____

1.015   You offer to sell a used car for $1,895. Yesterday you purchased the car for $1,755. What percentage markup are you charging? _____

1.016 You sell and service vacuum cleaners. Your price on a particular model is $135. However, to get a service contract, you offer to sell it for $115. How much discount are you giving as a percentage?

_____

1.017 You sell an automobile part for $9.98, which includes a 4% sales tax. If the article cost you $8.75, what percentage markup are you charging?

_____

# II. DATA INTERPRETATION

## OBJECTIVES

5. To interpret data in tabular form.
6. To perform line-graph analysis.
7. To perform bar-graph analysis.
8. To estimate service facility capacity.

A number of service occupations require interpretation of data, either in tabular form or in some type of graphic display. Automotive and food service industries illustrate data in tabular form and in graphic displays. For these services, as well as for others that involve equipment, a knowledge of *depreciation* costs is very useful.

## TABULAR DATA INTERPRETATION

In this section you will learn how to compute operating costs of V-8 and six-cylinder automobiles by using a table.

PROCEDURE

To determine automobile operating costs exclusive of finance charges, use the following data, which are based upon a Department of Transportation survey. To adjust the costs per mile under each category, multiply the cost given in the table by the ratio of (miles projected to be driven) to (miles given under each appropriate year). To obtain the cost per mile, divide the resulting cost figure by the miles projected to be driven.

|  | First Year (14,500 miles) | | Second Year (13,000 miles) | | Third Year (11,500 miles) | |
|---|---|---|---|---|---|---|
|  | V-8 Sedan | Six-cyl. Compact | V-8 Sedan | Six-cyl. Compact | V-8 Sedan | Six-cyl. Compact |
| Depreciation Cents Per Mile | 8.5 | 4.6 | 6.9 | 4.0 | 5.9 | 3.4 |
| Repairs and Maintenance Cents Per Mile | 0.7 | 0.7 | 1.0 | 1.0 | 2.3 | 1.6 |
| Gas and Oil Cents Per Mile | 2.1 | 1.8 | 2.1 | 1.8 | 2.1 | 1.8 |
| Insurance Cents Per Mile | 1.1 | 1.1 | 1.2 | 1.1 | 1.4 | 1.3 |
| Federal and State Taxes and Fees Cents Per Mile | 2.2 | 1.6 | 1.1 | 0.8 | 1.1 | 0.8 |
| Total Costs Cents Per Mile | $2,352 / 16 | $1,621 / 11.2 | $1,795 / 13.8 | $1,329 / 10.2 | $1,655 / 14.4 | $1,222 / 10.6 |

Model 1:  One of your company's salesmen estimates he will drive 20,000 miles this year and each of the next two years. As the service manager for the company's fleet of six-cylinder compact automobiles, you are asked to determine the total costs for each of the three years.

Start at the column headed First Year. Follow the column headed Six-cyl. Compact until you get to the row labeled Total Costs. Note that the figures given are 11.2¢ per mile and total costs of $1,621 based upon driving 14,500 miles. Since the salesman will be driving approximately 20,000 miles, compute the total costs using one of two methods as follows:

Method (1): $\frac{20,000}{14,500}$ x $1,621 = $2,236

Method (2): 20,000 x 11.2¢ = $2,240

For the second year, 20,000 x 10.2¢ = $2,040.

For the third year, 20,000 x 10.6¢ = $2,120.

From this point on, you will be using Method (2).

Model 2: How much depreciation should you take on a V-8 sedan in its first two years of driving if you assume you will drive 18,000 miles the first year and 16,500 miles the second?

From the table, find the V-8 column under the heading First Year: look at the row labeled Depreciation to find 8.5¢.

18,000 x 8.5¢ = $1,530. Do the same for the second year and find the depreciation as,

16,500 x 6.9¢ = $1,138.50 or $1,139.

Total two-year depreciation = $1,530 + 1,139 = $2,669.

▮▮▮ Compute the following operating costs as indicated, based on the preceding table.

2.1    Car = V-8 sedan
Year driven = third
Miles driven = 10,000
Compute gas and oil charges for the third year.

_____

2.2    Car = 6-cyl. compact
Years driven = first through third
Miles driven = 15,000 miles each year
Find the total depreciation.

_____

2.3    Car = V-8 sedan
Years driven = first and second
Miles driven = 16,500 miles first year and
      15,500 miles second year
Compute total cost of repairs and maintenance.

_____

17

2.4 Car = six-cyl. compact
   Year driven = second
   Miles driven = 14,000
   Compute insurance cost for second year.

_____

2.5 Car = six-cyl. compact
   Years driven = first through third year
   Miles driven = 15,000 first year; 14,000 second year;
    and 13,000 third year
   Compute total costs for all three years.

_____

## ~~~~ LINE-GRAPH ANALYSIS ~~~~

Graphs are used to show how one quantity
depends on or changes with another quantity.
One kind of graph is the line graph.

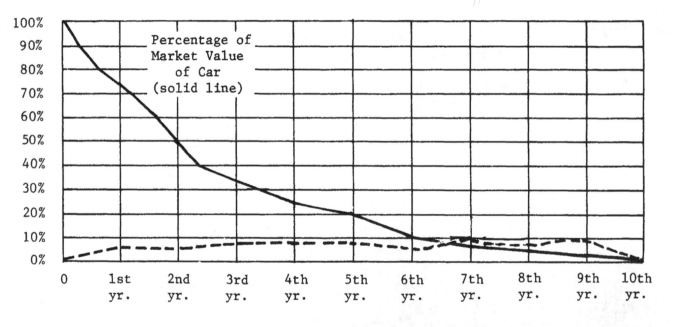

Maintenance and Repair Costs as Percentage of Car's Value
(dashed line)

18

PROCEDURE

To determine the market value of a car, find the anniversary year (number of years ago car was bought new) of the car on the preceding graph. Read straight up to where the solid data line and the percentage line intersect. Interpolate for intersections between percentages shown. Multiply that percentage by the original dollar of the car to find the dollar value for that particular year. To find the percentage of maintenance and repair costs, use the same procedure as before but locate the appropriate point on the dashed line. Note: Starting with the seventh year and beyond, the maintenance and repair costs are greater than the value of the car itself.

Model 1: You own a car purchased new 5 years ago. Its price then was $4,950. What is its value today?

Find the fifth year on the horizontal axis. Move up the perpendicular line from that point to where it intersects the solid line. Then move straight across to the left until you find the percentage figure, which is 20%. Proceed:

Value of car = $4,950 x 0.20 = $990.

Model 2: An automobile used for your business is three years old. It was purchased for $5,500 new. Find the difference between the current value of the automobile and its maintenance and repair costs for the third year.

From the graph the market value of the car = 35%. Also from the graph the maintenance and repairs = $5,500 x 0.08 = $440.

Value of car = $5,500 x 0.35 = $1,925

Costs of maintenance and repairs = $5,500 x 0.08 = $440

Difference = $1,925 - 440 = $1,485.

Using the value graph provided, compute the following market values and maintenance and repair costs.

2.6     Age of car = 6 years.
Original cost = $2,995.
Compute current market value.

2.7  Age of car = 4 years.
    Original cost = $3,850.
    Compute current market value.

_____

2.8  Age of car = 2 years.
    Original cost = $9,550.
    Compute current market value.

_____

2.9  Age of car = 7 years.
    Original cost = $3,500.
    Compute cost of maintenance and repairs.

_____

2.10  Age of car = 8 years.
    Original cost = $5,500.
    Compute the difference between the market
     value of the car and the maintenance and
     repair costs for the eighth year.
     (Note: You should get a negative value
     because maintenance and repair costs are
     more than the market value.)

_____

## BAR-GRAPH ANALYSIS

  Another kind of graph is the bar
graph. A bar graph compares quantities
by using rectangles of varying lengths,
each of which represents a certain
quantity.

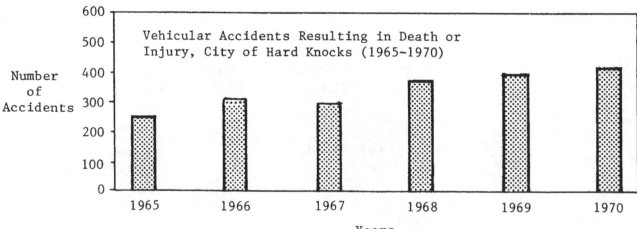

Model 1:   For the hypothetical city, the City of Hard
Knocks, in which year did most vehicular
accidents occur, and what was the number of
accidents?

By inspection you can see that the bar above
the year 1970 must be the answer to the first
part of the question.  Using the preceding
procedure, you can estimate that approximately
425 accidents occurred in that year.

Model 2:   What is the increase (percentage) in accidents
between 1966 and 1969?

Accidents for 1969 = 400
Accidents for 1966 = 310

$$\text{Percentage increase} = \frac{400 - 310}{310} = \frac{90}{310}$$
$$= 29\%.$$

 Using the same bar graph, work the following problems.

2.11   Which year had a decrease in the number of serious
accidents?

_____

2.12   Approximately how many accidents occurred between 1965 and
1970 inclusive?

_____

2.13   What was the percentage decrease in vehicular accidents
from 1966 to 1967?

_____

2.14   Which two consecutive years had the greatest percentage
increase in accidents?

_____

2.15    What was the percentage increase for Problem 2.14?

_____

2.16    How many more accidents happened in 1970 than in 1965?

_____

## FACILITY CAPACITY ESTIMATION

_Entrepeneurs_ in service occupations must familiarize themselves with shop and store layout and space requirements to ensure adequate capacity to service their customers.

Fortunately, some general rules exist that are helpful and relevant to the type of service that is offered. We shall discuss a few of these rules in this section.

---

PROCEDURE

To estimate floor space requirements in the food service business, one may plan on utilizing 20 square feet for each dining customer. You also need to plan on utilizing an additional one-third of the eating space for kitchen and storage space.

---

Model 1:    You are planning to expand your restaurant to seat an additional 50 customers. The current size of the dining area is 25 ft. x 35 ft. How much additional floor space should you plan for the dining area, and how much additional floor space should you plan for the kitchen and storage area?

a. Additional dining area
= 50 customers x 20 ft.$^2$ = 1,000 ft.$^2$

b. Additional kitchen area
= $\frac{1}{3}$ x 1,000 ft.$^2$ = 333 ft.$^2$

Model 2:    You are making plans to convert a large parlor and living room in a Victorian house you recently purchased into a specialty luncheon and tea room. If the combined rooms measure 35 ft. x 18.5 ft., how much seating capacity can you plan to have?

Area of rooms = 35 ft. x 18.5 ft. = 647.5 ft.$^2$

Number of seats = $\frac{647.5 \text{ ft.}^2}{20 \text{ ft.}^2}$ = 32

```
PROCEDURE

To estimate the garage area required to service automobiles,
multiply the number of vehicles you estimate your shop can
service by 250 ft.²  Double the resulting figure to allow
for free space for vehicle passage.
```

Model 1:  The garage you work for as an auto mechanic
measures 250 ft. by 130 ft.  Assuming full
capacity, how many cars can be reasonably
parked for servicing?

Area of garage = 250 ft. x 130 ft. = 32,500 ft.²

Space available for parking = $\frac{32,500 \text{ ft.}^2}{2}$

$= 16,250 \text{ ft.}^2$

Number of vehicles = $\frac{16,250 \text{ ft.}^2}{250 \text{ ft.}^2} = 65$

Model 2:  The service manager of your shop estimates
that you can increase your servicing capabilities
by an additional 15 cars.  How much more floor
space is required?

$15 \times 250 \text{ ft.}^2 = 3,750 \text{ ft.}^2$

Additional space required = $2 \times 3,750 \text{ ft.}^2$
$= 7,500 \text{ ft.}^2$

████  Work the following facility capacity problems.

2.17  Determine the seating capacity of a restaurant measuring

100 ft. by 35 ft. _____

2.18  You are planning to open a restaurant to seat 110

customers.  How much floor space will you need (seating

capacity only)? _____

2.19  Find the total space needed to seat 75 customers and to

provide for appropriate kitchen and storage area as well.

_____

2.20    You must add to your kitchen area to accommodate an increase of 60 customers. How much additional kitchen and storage area will you need? _____

2.21    A garage measures 160 ft. x 110 ft. How many automobiles can be parked for servicing? _____

2.22    Your service agency projects servicing 110 cars daily. How many square feet will you need?

_____

2.23    The garage you own has dimensions of 200 ft. x 85 ft. You estimate the demand for servicing at your facility next year will average 86 cars daily. Do you have sufficient space assuming one-half of the vehicles are in the shop at any one time? _____

2.24    The average daily count of cars serviced at your garage is 48. You estimate a turnover factor of three during the eight-hour shift. Since one-third of the vehicles need space at any given time, what is the garage area needed? _____

---

    Review the material in this section in preparation for the Self Test. This Self Test will check your mastery of this particular section as well as your knowledge of the previous section.

# CONSUMER MATHEMATICS 6: LIFEPAC TEST

Compute the following financial transactions (each answer, 3 points).

1.      Price of item = $38.22
        Cash tendered = $50.02
        Change due?

        _____

2.      Retail price = $4.65
        Sales tax rate = 4%
        Total bill?

        _____

Compute interest charges for the following credit transaction (each answer, 4 points).

3.      Amount of loan = $850
        Monthly payment amount = $42.50
        Duration of payments = 24 months
        True annual interest rate?

        _____

Work the following discount and markup problems (each answer, 3 points).

4.      List price = $720
        Discount rate = 12%
        Amount of discount?

        _____

5.      Cost of article = $110
        Percent markup = 22%
        Selling price?

        _____

Perform the following facility capacity problems (each answer, 3 points).

6.      Seating capacity = 110
        Area of dining room?
        Area of kitchen and storage?

        _____

7.      Number of cars parked at any one time = 48
        Required area of service garage?

        _____

Apply the appropriate mathematical operations to the following specific occupations (each answer, 3 points).

8.        Resistance = 2 ohms
           Current = 60 amps
           Voltage ?

                             _____

9.        Gear 1 = 30 teeth
           Speed, gear 1 = 150 r.p.m.
           Speed, gear 2 = 75 r.p.m.
           Teeth, gear 2 ?

                             _____

10.       Weight 1 = 150 lb.  (fulcrum)
           Weight 2 = 450 lb.
           $d_1$ = 15 ft.

           $d_2$ ?                   _____

11.       Diameter of pulley $a$ = 4"
           Diameter of pulley $c$ = 6"
           Diameter of pulley $d$ = 5"
           r.p.m. of pulley $b$ = 1,000
           Pulleys $b$ and $c$ are keyed together.
           What is the r.p.m. of pulley $d$?

                             _____

12.       Diameter of axle = 3.5" (axle)
           Axis of handle = 21"
           Weight lifted = 180 lb.
           Force, $F$ ?

                             _____

13.       Number of dinners = 165.
           Individual portion = 6 oz.
           Size of can = 45 oz.
           Number of cans required?

                             _____

14.       Amount of chicken = 48 lb.
           Number of patrons served?

                             _____

15.       Weight of adult = 135 lb.
           Recommended protein intake ?

                           _____

16.       Weight of man = 187 lb.
           Speed of running = 8 minutes for 1 mile
           Calories burned off ?

                         _____

17.       Labor rate = $8.75 per hour
           Hours worked = 16
           Total price of services = $273
           Overhead rate ?       _____

Answer the following questions based on the given line graph (each answer, 3 points).

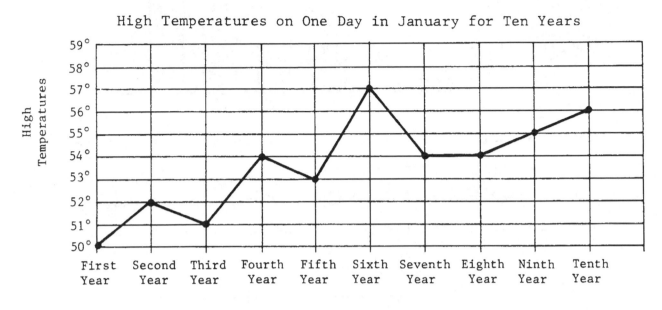

High Temperatures on One Day in January for Ten Years

Years

18.    According to the given line graph, what is the trend in temperature--warmer or cooler? _____

19.    How many degrees warmer was the fourth temperature from the third temperature? _____

20.    Which years had the same temperatures on the given day?

_____

21.    How much did the temperature cool off from the sixth year to the seventh year on the given day (as a percentage)?

_____

22.    What is the average daily temperature for all ten years?

_____

Based on the following graph, perform the required data interpretations (each answer, 3 points).

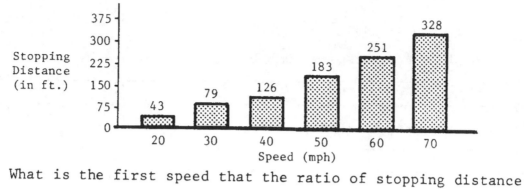

23.    What is the first speed that the ratio of stopping distance to speed is greater than 3 to 1? _____

24.    While speed doubles from 20 mph to 40 mph, the stopping distance almost triples (2.93). Does the same relationship for stopping distance hold when speed doubles from 30 mph to 60 mph? _____

25.    In reducing one's speed from 70 mph to 50 mph, how much of a percentage decrease in stopping distance is realized?

_____

26.    Between what two consecutive speeds does the greatest percentage increase in stopping distance occur?

_____

Use the following tabular data to answer Questions 27 through 31 (each answer, 3 points).

| | Automobile Cost | Trade-in Value | Useful Life | Annual Depreciation |
|---|---|---|---|---|
| 27. | $4,500 | $500 | 5 yr. | _____ |
| 28. | $10,000 | $2,800 | 6 yr. | _____ |
| 29. | $8,150 | $3,000 | 5 yr. | _____ |
| 30. | $12,995 | $4,700 | 8 yr. | _____ |
| 31. | $2,685 | $685 | $3\frac{1}{2}$ yr. | _____ |

4

## SELF TEST 2

Answer Questions 2.01 through 2.05 based upon the following table (each answer, 3 points).

Selected Service Careers, Numbers, and Pay

| | Male | | | Female | | |
|---|---|---|---|---|---|---|
| | Number 1960 | Number 1970 | Median Earnings 1969 ($) | Number 1960 | Number 1970 | Median Earnings 1969 ($) |
| Accountants | 414,000 | 526,000 | 10,627 | 82,000 | 187,000 | 5,818 |
| Computer Specialists | 9,000 | 207,000 | 11,993 | 4,000 | 51,000 | 7,763 |
| Buyers, Sales Managers | 347,000 | 685,000 | 11,612 | 71,000 | 135,000 | 5,530 |
| Managers and Administrators | 2,166,000 | 2,487,000 | 12,196 | 318,000 | 354,000 | 6,011 |
| Self-employed Managers | 1,559,000 | 768,000 | 8,857 | 225,000 | 145,000 | 3,886 |
| Sales Workers | 3,063,000 | 3,378,000 | 8,451 | 1,736,000 | 2,247,000 | 2,338 |
| Bank Tellers | 157,000 | 175,000 | 3,860 | 95,000 | 218,000 | 4,190 |

2.01    According to the tabular data presented, what is the largest single category of service careers in terms of employment of both sexes? _____

2.02    The growth in computer specialists was remarkable during 1960-1970 for both sexes.  Calculate the percentages of growth for both sexes in this service occupation.

_____

2.03    Which service-career category experienced decline

        for both sexes in the data period?    _____

2.04    Which service occupation had the lowest median salary for

        males; for females?    _____

2.05    How much more did female bank tellers earn than male bank

        tellers as a percentage of median earnings in 1969?

        _____

Answer Questions 2.06 through 2.010 based upon the following line
graph (each answer, 3 points).

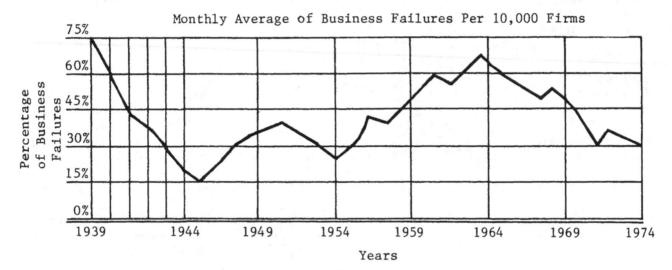

2.06    According to the line graph, approximately which year

        had the largest percentage of business failures?

        _____

2.07    Which year had the lowest rate of business failures

        (approximately)?    _____

2.08    During which five-year period was the greatest improvement

        registered (percentage-wise) in the number of business

        failures?    _____

2.09    From Question 2.08, approximately what was the range in

        total percentages of business failures during that

        same period?    _____

2.010   Since about 1960, what has been the general trend in

business failures as a percentage of total firms--up

or down?   _____

Answer Questions 2.011 through 2.015 based upon the following bar
graph (each question, 3 points).

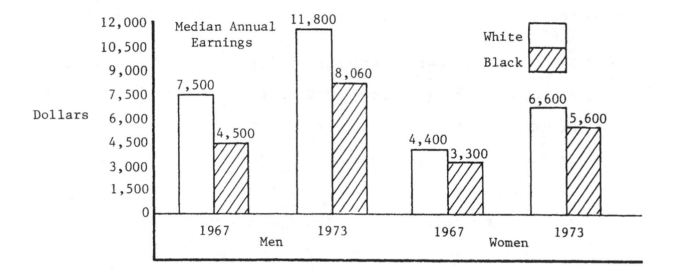

*Median* earnings are earnings in the middle of all earnings ranked from
the lowest earnings to the highest earnings.

2.011   For the year 1967, what was the difference in median

earnings between white males and black males?

_____

2.012   What was the percentage difference in median earnings

between black males and white males for 1967?

_____

2.013   What was the percentage difference in median earnings

between black males and white males during 1973?

_____

2.014    In comparing your answers to Questions 2.012 and 2.013, did the black males' median earnings improve relative to white males' median earnings?  _____

2.015    Considering only whites, what was the difference in dollars between the median earnings for males in 1973 and that for females in the same year?  _____

Perform the following facility capacity calculations (each answer, 3 points).

2.016    You estimate that it requires fifty minutes to serve 85 customers through a cafeteria line.  If your normal lunch crowd averages 200 customers, about how much time will it take for the lunch crowd to go through the cafeteria line (assuming a constant flow of customers)?  _____

2.017    Your dining room facility seats 150 patrons.  The present eating area is 60 ft. by 50 ft.  You desire to expand it by 20%.  How much should the whole area contain in square feet after it is expanded?

_____

2.018    Your garage can service 180 vehicles daily.  If the garage measures 250 ft. by 180 ft., how many vehicles can you have in the garage at any one time?

_____

2.019    You require space to service 65 vehicles at any one time. Will a facility measuring 165 ft. by 130 ft. be adequate?  _____

28

Perform the following computations based upon material covered in Section I (each answer, 4 points).

2.020    You offer senior citizens a 20% discount on their meal prices served at your cafeteria. Assuming that an average of 150 senior citizens eat daily at your cafeteria and that the average price of their meals before discount is $2.95, how much total discount do you give on an average daily basis? _____

2.021    You are selling automobiles at a 15% markup from the wholesale cost to you as a dealer. If a particular model costs you $3,050, at what retail price will you offer it?

_____

2.022    Diamonds are generally marked up 100% from wholesale. If you offer a discount of 25% on a diamond ring that originally cost you $275 wholesale, at what price are you offering the ring? _____

2.023    A meal costs $5.75. You offer a 10% discount. The sales tax is 4%. How much should you charge the customer?

_____

2.024    Assuming the customer gives you a $10 bill for the meal in Question 2.023, how much change should you give him?

_____

2.025    Your service contract for washer repair maintenance is offered at $48 per year. If a customer wants to pay it off in equal monthly installments for one year and if the true annual interest charge is 18%, what should his monthly payment be? _____

2.026   You offer to pay back $1,500 on a $1,000 note over a
        two-year period.  What true annual interest rate are
        you paying on this loan?

        _____

2.027   You charge customers $18.95 for lube service, parts, and
        labor.  Assuming you take one hour's labor at $15,
        and the parts cost $3.50, what is the tax rate on the
        parts?                          _____

# III. SERVICE OCCUPATIONS

9. To apply correct mathematical operations in specific occupations.

10. To determine prices for services rendered.

In this section you will be exposed to a number of different applications of mathematics appropriate for selected service occupations. Not only will these problems give you practice in mathematical operations, but they should also increase your appreciation for the role mathematics plays in many occupational activities.

## AUTOMOTIVE SERVICES

This section covers how to make the following calculations: resistance, number of teeth on a gear, speed, and mechanical advantage.

---

PROCEDURE

To determine the resistance in ohms to a given current, expressed in amperes, set up by a given voltage, divide the voltage by the current.

$$R = \frac{E}{I}$$

---

Model 1: What resistance must a car's motor have to start the car if 55 amperes are taken from the car's 12-bolt battery when the key is turned?

$$R = \frac{E}{I} = \frac{12}{55}$$

Therefore, $R = 0.22$ ohm.

Model 2: A resistance of 0.2 ohm will permit a flow of how much current from a 12-volt battery?

$$I = \frac{E}{R} = \frac{12}{0.2}$$

Therefore, $I = 60$ amperes.

```
PROCEDURE

To determine the number of teeth on a gear:  the ratio of
the number of teeth on two drive gears is *inversely* related
to the ratio of their respective r.p.m. (revolutions per
minute).
```

$$\frac{\text{No. teeth gear 1}}{\text{No. teeth gear 2}} = \frac{\text{r.p.m. gear 2}}{\text{r.p.m. gear 1}}$$

Model 1:  A transmission main drive gear has 25 teeth and
rotates 500 r.p.m.  It drives a countershaft
drive gear at 250 r.p.m.  How many teeth
does the countershaft drive gear have?

$$\frac{25}{\text{No. teeth gear 2}} = \frac{250}{500}$$

No. of teeth on gear 2 = 50.

Model 2:  In first gear, or low gear, an automobile's
engine runs about three times as fast
at the propeller shaft.  In second gear,
the engine does not have to run as fast;
usually it runs about $1\frac{2}{3}$ times faster
than the propeller shaft.  Finally, in
third, or high gear, the engine runs
at the same speed as the propeller shaft.

Suppose an engine is running 2,000 r.p.m.
in second gear.  How fast is the propeller
shaft running?

$$2,000 \div 1\frac{2}{3} = 2,000 \times \frac{3}{5} = 1,200 \text{ r.p.m.}$$

```
PROCEDURE

To determine the mechanical advantage of a particular
machine, use the following guidelines:  the ideal mechanical
advantage of a machine = distance ratio = distance moved
by a force operating a machine divided by distance load moved.
```

The preceding procedure may be
utilized in several machine relationships
involving distance, force, speed, and
weight.  The following models are three
such examples.

Model 1:   Fulcrums

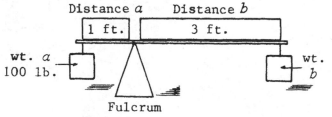

If the two weights on this fulcrum are
balanced, then the unknown weight must be
$33\frac{1}{3}$ lb.:

$$\text{weight}_a \times \text{distance}_a = \text{weight}_b \times \text{distance}_b$$

$$100 \times 1 = \text{wt.}_b \times 3$$

$$\text{wt.}_b = \frac{100}{3} = 33\frac{1}{3} \text{ lb.}$$

Model 2:   Pulleys

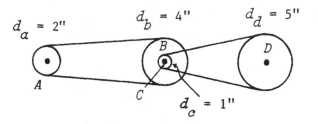

The r.p.m. of each pulley is related to its
diameter.  Thus, if pulley $A$, which has a
2" diameter, rotates at 500 r.p.m., then
pulley $B$, which has a 4" diameter, or twice
the diameter of pulley $A$, must rotate at one-
half the speed of pulley $A$, or 250 r.p.m.

$$\frac{d_a}{d_b} = \frac{\text{r.p.m.}_b}{\text{r.p.m.}_a}$$

$$\frac{2}{4} = \frac{\text{r.p.m.}_b}{500}$$

$$\text{r.p.m.}_b = \frac{1,000}{4} = 250 \text{ r.p.m.}$$

Pulley $C$'s diameter is 1"; but, because pulley
$C$ is keyed to the same shaft as pulley $B$, it has
to rotate at the speed of $B$, or 250 r.p.m.
Pulley $C$ drives pulley $D$, whose diameter is
5".  Then, for pulley $D$

$$\frac{d_c}{d_d} = \frac{\text{r.p.m.}_d}{\text{r.p.m.}_c}$$

$$\frac{1}{5} = \frac{\text{r.p.m.}_d}{250}$$

$$\text{r.p.m.}_d = \frac{250}{5} = 50 \text{ r.p.m.}$$

Model 3:   Axles

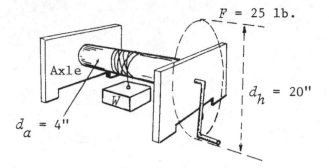

The axis of the handle is the diameter of
the circle formed by moving the handle
around one complete turn.   In this case, the
diameter is 20 inches.   $F$, which is the force
exerted on the handle to lift the weight, is
25 pounds.   The diameter of the axle if 4".   To
figure how much the weight weighs, use the
following equation and compute as shown.

$$F \times d_h = W \times d_a$$
$$25 \times 20 = W \times 4$$
$$W = \frac{500}{4} = 125 \text{ lb.}$$

Solve the following automotive-services problems based
on the examples shown previously.

3.1     Voltage = 18 v
        Current = 36 amps
        Resistance = ?

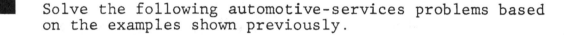

3.2     Voltage = 12 v
        Current = 48 amps
        Resistance = ?

3.3     Resistance = 0.1 ohm
        Current = 60 amps
        Voltage = ?

3.4     Voltage = 120 v
        Current = 50 amps
        Resistance = ?

3.5  Engine speed = 1,850 r.p.m.
    Transmission in second gear
    Propeller-shaft speed = ?

_____

3.6  Engine speed = 2,100 r.p.m.
    Transmission in first gear
    Propeller-shaft speed = ?

_____

3.7  Engine speed = 2,400 r.p.m.
    Propeller-shaft speed = 2,400 r.p.m.
    Transmission in which gear?

_____

3.8  Propeller-shaft speed = 650 r.p.m.
    Transmission in first gear
    Engine speed = ?

_____

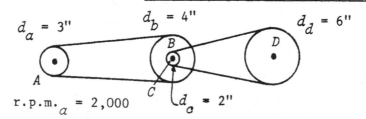

3.9  In this pulley diagram how fast do pulleys $B$ and

    $C$ rotate, assuming they are keyed together?

_____

3.10  Based on your answer in Problem 3.9, how fast must pulley $D$

    rotate?

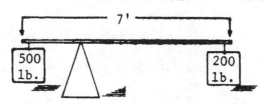

3.11  In this fulcrum the weights are perfectly balanced. How

    far must the fulcrum be located from the 200 lb. weight if

    the bar is 7 feet long?

_____

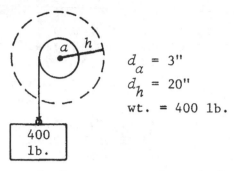

$d_a$ = 3"

$d_h$ = 20"

wt. = 400 lb.

400 lb.

3.12    Given this axle, how much force must be used

to lift the weight?                    _____

Two of the responsibilities that
restaurants and cafeterias have are to
know how many cases of canned foods and
how many pounds of meat are needed to
feed their customers.  This section
explains how to determine these questions.

---

PROCEDURE

To determine the number of cases of a certain canned food item
needed to feed diners, multiply the number to be served by the
size of the individual portion.  Then divide the resulting
figure by the capacity of a standard can of the food item.
Finally, divide the resulting number of cans needed by 12 to
obtain the number of cases.

---

Model 1:    You serve 380 customers at dinner.  You plan to
serve tomato juice, which comes in 46 oz. cans.
Assuming you plan to serve each customer a
5 oz. portion, how many cases of tomato juice
will you need?

No. of ounces needed = 380 x 5 = 1,900

No. of cans needed = $\frac{1,900}{46}$ = 41.3, or 42 cans

No. of cases needed = $\frac{42}{12}$ = 3.5

Model 2:    A #10 can yields 120 oz. of pineapple.  You plan to
give each diner an 8-oz. portion.  You estimate
you will feed 240 patrons.  How many #10 cans
will you need?

No. of ounces needed = 240 x 8 = 1,920

No of #10 cans needed = $\frac{1,920}{120}$ = 16

PROCEDURE

To calculate the number of pounds of meat required to feed
diners, for poultry divide the number to be served by 2.5;
for meat with little or no bone, divide the number to be
served by 3.5; and for fish fillets divide the number to
be served by 3.5.

Model 1:  Your restaurant serves ground round steak.
          You estimate you will serve 150 patrons
          in any given day.  How many pounds of round
          steak should you prepare?

          No. of pounds = $\frac{150}{3.5}$ = 42.86, or 43 lb.

Model 2:  You have prepared 50 lb. of fish fillets for
          the dinner meal.  You serve 125 customers.
          Do you have enough fish prepared?

          No. of servings = 50 x 3.5 = 175
          You have an excess of 50 servings, so the answer
          is yes.

███      Perform the following calculations based on the food-
         service section.

3.13     No. of diners = 250
         Portions of juice served = 4 oz. per diner
         Size of juice can = 48 oz.
         How many cases of juice required?

         _____

3.14     Size of juice can = 44 oz.
         Portions of juice served = 6 oz.
         Number of cases used = 2
         How many patrons can be served?

         _____

3.15     No. of patrons = 225
         Portions of beets served = 8 oz.
         Size of beet can = 45 oz.
         How many cans of beets required?

         _____

3.16    No. of customers = 160
        Meat served = chicken
        How many pounds of chicken required?

        _____

3.17    No. of diners = 240
        Meat served = meat with little bone
        Amount of meat required?

        _____

3.18    Meat to be served = fish fillet
        Amount of stock = 86 lb.
        How many customers can be served fish?

        _____


## PERSONAL APPEARANCE SERVICES

        This section explains how to
determine the recommended protein intake
for an average adult and how to determine
the amount of calories used per mile of
jogging.

---

PROCEDURE

To determine the recommended minimum protein intake in kilograms
for the average adult, multiply the weight in pounds of
the individual by 0.45.  For each kilogram of weight, the
intake should be 1 gram of protein.

---

Model 1:   The weight of an adult woman is 125 lb.
           How much protein should she intake?

           Converted weight = 125 x 0.45 = 56.25 kg
           Amount of protein = 56.25 x 1 = 56.25 g

Model 2:   If a man intakes 65 g of protein daily,
           his recommended intake, how much does
           he weigh in pounds?

           65 g protein = 65 kg of weight

           Weight in pounds = $\frac{65}{0.45}$ = 144 lb.

Another important energy unit is
the *calorie*.  A calorie is the unit
used to express the heat-producing, or
energy-producing, value of food.  Too
many calories, of course, add extra fat
to the body.  A person can watch his
calorie intake when he eats and can
burn off excess calories through vigorous
exercise.  Jogging is a very popular
method of exercising.  As a rule of
thumb, one may go by the following
procedure to determine calorie loss
from running.

---

PROCEDURE

The amount of calories used per mile of jogging is
determined by an individual's weight and speed of running.
If a person runs the mile in six minutes, his calorie-use
factor is approximately $\frac{2}{3}$ of his weight.  If he runs
the mile in eight minutes, his calorie-use factor is 65%
of his weight; If he runs the mile in ten minutes, his
calorie-use factor is 62% of his weight.

---

Model 1:   A man weighs 180 lb.  He jogs a mile in
           10 minutes.  How many calories has he used
           up?

           Calories used = weight x use factor for 10-
                               min. mile
                         = 180 x 0.62 = 112

Model 2:   A woman weighs 130 lb.  She wishes to burn
           off 85 calories.  Approximately how fast
           must she run a mile to do so?

           Calorie-use factor = $\frac{85}{130}$ = 65%

           The 65% calorie-use factor is associated with
           the 8-minute mile, so she must run the mile
           in eight minutes.


████    Perform the following calculations based on the personal-
        appearance section.

3.19    Person = adult male
        Weight = 165 lb.
        How much protein should he intake?

---

39

3.20    Person = adult female
        Weight = 112 lb.
        How much protein should she consume?

_____

3.21    Person = adult male
        Amount of protein ingested = 69.75 g
        How much does he weigh?

_____

3.22    Weight of male = 174 lb.
        Jogging speed = 1 mile in 6 minutes
        How many calories used?

_____

3.23    Weight of female = 135 lb.
        Jogging speed = 1 mile in 10 minutes
        How many calories used?

_____

3.24    Calories burned off = 90
        Weight of male = 139 lb.
        Jogging speed?

_____

## PRICES FOR SERVICES RENDERED

One important aspect of working in the service occupations is determining a fair price for your services. Typically, such a price is made up of your direct labor cost, usually figured at an hourly rate, and the overhead rate (usually a percentage of the labor cost). The overhead rate pays for such things as rent, utilities, administrative costs, and equipment use and depreciation.

This section will not include how to determine overhead rates. However, they exist, they vary from business to business and from place to place, and they must be added to the cost of labor to determine the total price for the services rendered.

40

```
┌─────────────────────────────────────────────────────────────────┐
│                                                                   │
│  PROCEDURE                                                        │
│                                                                   │
│  To calculate the price for any job performed, multiply          │
│  the hourly wage rate of the employee(s) involved by the         │
│  number of hours worked and add an overhead cost usually         │
│  expressed as a percentage of the total labor cost.              │
│                                                                   │
└─────────────────────────────────────────────────────────────────┘
```

Model 1:   You must give an estimate to service an automobile. The hourly rate for labor is $7.50. You estimate the job will take $2\frac{1}{2}$ hours. The overhead rate at your shop is 85%. You also figure that parts to be used total $25.50 retail. How much is the job estimate?

Labor costs = $7.50 x $2\frac{1}{2}$ = $18.75
Overhead costs = $18.75 x 0.85 = $15.94
Cost of parts = $25.50
Estimate of total cost = $18.75 + 15.94 + 25.50
                                    = $60.19

Model 2:   Hairdressers in your shop earn $5.50 per hour. Your overhead rate is 50%. If a wash, rinse, and set take 2 hours, and no charge is made for materials used, how much should the hairdresser charge?

Cost of labor = $5.50 x 2 = $11.00
Cost of overhead = $11.00 x 0.50 = $5.50
Total charge = $11.00 + 5.50 = $16.50

Model 3:   Your heavy-duty mechanics earn $15.00 per hour. Your light-duty servicemen earn $6.50 per hour. Assume a customer wants his engine tuned, oiled, and greased. If the job takes $1\frac{1}{2}$ hours of a mechanic's time, $1\frac{1}{2}$ hours of a serviceman's time, and the overhead rate is 100%, what are the total labor plus overhead charges?

Cost of mechanic's labor = $15.00 x $1\frac{1}{2}$ = $22.50
Cost of serviceman's labor = $6.50 x $1\frac{1}{2}$ = $9.75
Total labor charges = $22.50 + 9.75 = $32.25
Cost of overhead = $32.25 x 1.00 = $32.25
Total charges = $32.25 + 32.25 = $64.50

■■■   Work the following pricing problems for services rendered.

3.25    Labor rate = $8.50 per hour
Labor time = $4\frac{3}{4}$ hours
Overhead rate = 85%
Retail price for parts = $17.75
Total job cost?

3.26    Labor rate = $7.00 per hour
        Labor time = 15 hours
        Overhead rate = 110%
        Retail price of parts = $38.75
        Total job cost?

        _____


3.27    Labor rate = $8.00 per hour
        Labor time = 6 hours
        Retail price of parts = $0
        Total job cost = $86.00
        Overhead rate?

        _____


3.28    Hourly rate, worker $A$ = $15.00
        Hourly rate, worker $B$ = $8.00
        Hourly rate, worker $C$ = $5.25
        Labor time, worker $A$ = $2\frac{1}{2}$ hours
        Labor time, worker $B$ = 1 hour
        Labor time, worker $C$ = $\frac{3}{4}$ hour
        Overhead rate = 75%
        Retail price of goods = $125.50
        Total cost of job?

        _____


3.29    Labor time = $4\frac{1}{2}$ hours
        Overhead rate = 95%
        Retail price of parts = $134.75
        Total cost of job = $241.98
        What is hourly rate for labor?

        _____

_____

        Before you take this last Self Test, you may want to do one or more of
these self checks.

1.  _____  Read the objectives. Determine if you can do them.

2.  _____  Restudy the material related to any objectives that you cannot do.

3.  _____  Use the SQ3R study procedure to review the material:

        a.  **S**can the sections,
        b.  **Q**uestion yourself again (review the questions you wrote
            initially),
        c.  **R**ead to answer your questions,
        d.  **R**ecite the answers to yourself, and
        e.  **R**eview areas you didn't understand.

4.  _____  Review all activities, and Self Tests, writing a correct answer for
        each wrong answer.

# SELF TEST 3

Answer the following automotive services questions (each answer, 3 points).

3.01    Voltage = 12 v
        Current = 60 amps
        Resistance?

_____

3.02    Current = 55 amps
        Resistance = 0.11 ohm
        Voltage?

_____

3.03    Main drive gear = 35 teeth
        Countershaft drive gear = 70 teeth
        Speed of main drive gear = 450 r.p.m.
        Speed of countershaft drive gear?

_____

3.04    Engine speed = 3,000 r.p.m.
        Transmission in first gear
        Speed of shaft?

_____

3.05    Speed of propeller shaft = 825 r.p.m.
        Transmission in second gear
        Speed of engine?

3.06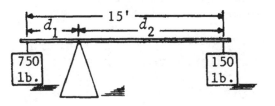

        In this fulcrum, for the weights to be in balance,
        what do the distances $d_1$ and $d_2$ have to be?

_____

3.07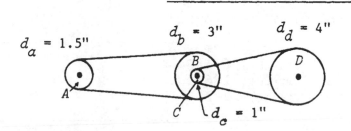

        Speed of pulley $A$ = 300 r.p.m.
        Find speeds of pulleys $B$, $C$, and $D$.

_____

43

3.08

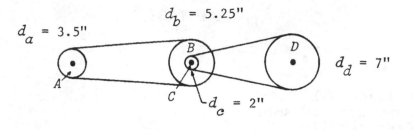

$d_a = 3.5"$  $d_b = 5.25"$  $d_d = 7"$  $d_c = 2"$

Speed of pulley $D$ = 100 r.p.m.
Find speed of pulley $A$.

3.09

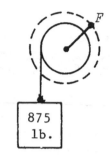

875 lb.

Diameter of axle = 4"
Axis of handle = 35"
Weight lifted = 875 lb.
Find the force, $F$.

Answer the following food service and personal appearance questions (each answer, 3 points).

3.010    Size of #10 tomato juice can = 115 oz.
         Size of individual portion = 7 oz.
         Number of portions served = 275
         Find how many #10 cans are needed.

3.011    Meat served = chicken
         Pounds of chicken available = 66
         Find number of servings.

3.012    Calories burned off = 84
         Weight of woman = 126 lb.
         Find the jogging rate.

Compute the following costs of services problems (each answer, 3 points).

3.013   Hourly rate of labor = $12.00
        Duration of job = 3½ hours
        Overhead rate = 66⅔%
        Price of parts = $112.50
        Find total cost of job.

        _____

3.014   Total cost of job = $147.51
        Duration of job = 5 hours
        Price of parts = $32.50
        Overhead rate = 55%
        What is hourly rate of labor?

        _____

3.015   Labor rate = $14 per hour
        Hours worked = 40
        Overhead rate = 125%
        Retail price of good furnished = $85
        Sales tax rate = 6%
        Total bill for services and parts?

        _____

Work the following facility capacity problems (each answer, 4 points).

3.016   The area of your dining room measures 1,400 ft.$^2$  How many people will it seat?  _____

3.017   Your garage measures 300 ft. by 165 ft.  How many automobiles can your garage service in a day, assuming an average car can be serviced in half a day.

_____

3.018   Your cafeteria line requires 8 minutes on the average for each customer to proceed through the line and pay the cashier.  The average time space between each customer is 30 seconds.  If the line is open for 1½ hours for lunch, how many customers can you serve for lunch?

_____

3.019   Your beauty salon has 8 stations, each requiring 36 square feet of space.  Additional space, such as passageways, receptionist area, storage, and restrooms add another 216 square feet to your salon area.  You plan to add 2 more stations.  Assume you maintain the same area for each station, and the additional space remains proportionally the same as previously.  How much area will your remodeled salon require?

_____

Answer Questions 3.020 through 3.022 based upon the following graph (each answer, 2 points).

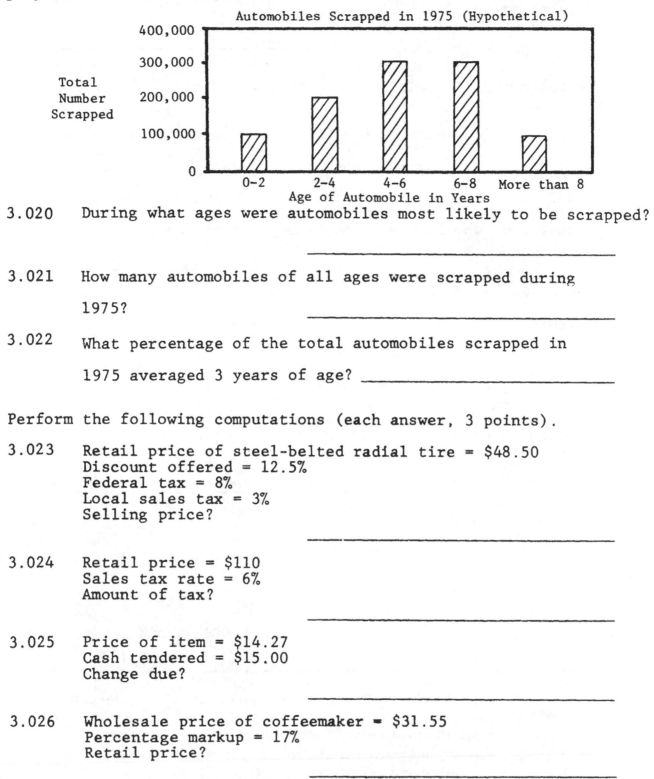

Automobiles Scrapped in 1975 (Hypothetical)

3.020   During what ages were automobiles most likely to be scrapped?

_____

3.021   How many automobiles of all ages were scrapped during

1975?   _____

3.022   What percentage of the total automobiles scrapped in

1975 averaged 3 years of age? _____

Perform the following computations (each answer, 3 points).

3.023   Retail price of steel-belted radial tire = $48.50
Discount offered = 12.5%
Federal tax = 8%
Local sales tax = 3%
Selling price?

_____

3.024   Retail price = $110
Sales tax rate = 6%
Amount of tax?

_____

3.025   Price of item = $14.27
Cash tendered = $15.00
Change due?

_____

3.026   Wholesale price of coffeemaker = $31.55
Percentage markup = 17%
Retail price?

_____

47

3.027     Cost of meal = $8.50
Discount offered = 15%
Sales tax = 5%
Actual price?

_____

Work the following financial transactions (each answer, 4 points).

3.028     Your station charges $6.50 for a lubrication job. As a promotion you sell six coupons for lubrication jobs for $32.50. What percentage discount are you offering for customers who purchase the 6-coupon lube book?

_____

3.029     You borrow $2,500. You are to pay back the loan in 36 monthly payments of $79.50. What true annual interest are you paying? _____

3.030     Price of article = $315.50
Down payment = $31.55
Monthly payment amount = $16.50
Duration of payments = 20 months
True annual interest rate?

_____

```
┌─────────┐
│ 75  ╱   │
│   ╱  94 │
└─────────┘
```

Score    _____

✓ Teacher check _____

                                   Initial       Date

Before taking the LIFEPAC Test, you may want to do one or more of these self checks.

1. _____ Read the objectives. Check to see if you can do them.
2. _____ Restudy the material related to any objective that you cannot do.
3. _____ Use the SQ3R study procedure to review the material.
4. _____ Review activities, Self Tests, and LIFEPAC Glossary.
5. _____ Restudy areas of weakness indicated by the last Self Test.

# GLOSSARY

*calorie.*   A unit of energy supplied by food.

*depreciation.*   A lessening or lowering in value of a commodity based on its age.

*discount.*   A deduction from the amount of the regular price of a good.

*entrepreneur.*   A person who organizes and manages a business.

*interest.*   Amount of money paid for the use of money.

*interest rate.*   The rate per cent per unit of time of such a payment.

*inversely.*   Reversed in tendency; opposite in nature or effect.

*markup.*   The percentage or amount added to the cost of a commodity to take care of profit and overhead to establish the selling price of the commodity.

*median.*   The value in a series of values that has as many values above as below.

*overhead.*   General expenses or charges of a business such as rent, lighting, heating, taxes, and repairs, which cannot be charged against a particular operation.

*principal.*   Sum of money on which interest is paid.

*profit.*   The gain from any transaction.

*tender.*   Amount offered in payment of a debt.